Piano
Specimen Sight-Reading Tests

ABRSM Initial Grade

Learning to sight-read helps you to develop quick recognition of keys, tonality and common rhythm patterns. It also helps you to learn to keep going even when you make mistakes, and work music out for yourself – which makes learning new pieces quicker and easier.

In the exam, you will be asked to play a short piece of music that you have not seen before. You will be given half a minute to look through and, if you wish, try out all or any part of the test before you are asked to play it to the examiner for assessment.

Any fingering shown on the tests is for guidance only. You are welcome to use any fingering that produces a successful musical outcome.

These requirements are valid until further notice. Reference must always be made to the syllabus for the year in which the exam is to be taken, in case any changes have been made to the requirements.

www.abrsm.org/piano

First published in 2020 by ABRSM (Publishing) Ltd, a wholly owned subsidiary of ABRSM
© 2020 by The Associated Board of the Royal Schools of Music
Unauthorised photocopying is illegal

Music origination by Moira Roach
Cover by Kate Benjamin & Andy Potts
Printed in England by Halstan & Co. Ltd, Amersham, Bucks, on materials from sustainable source
P16066

Grandly

1

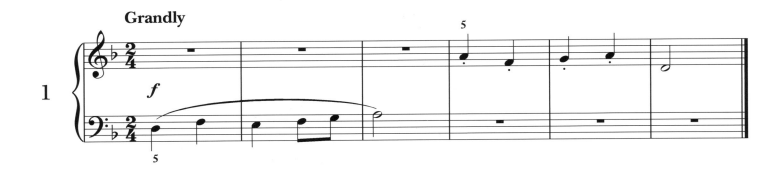

Lively

2

Smoothly

3

Moderato

4

Grandly

5

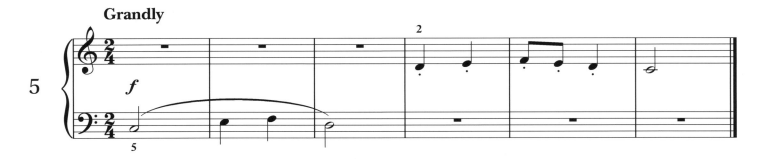

6 Moderato

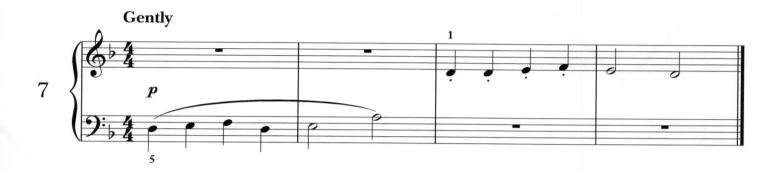

7 Gently

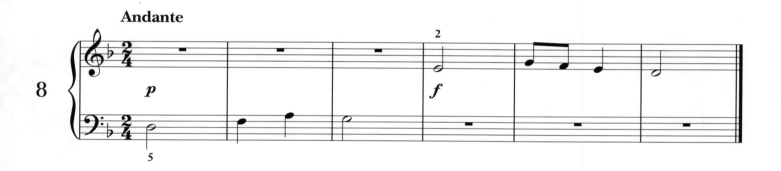

8 Andante

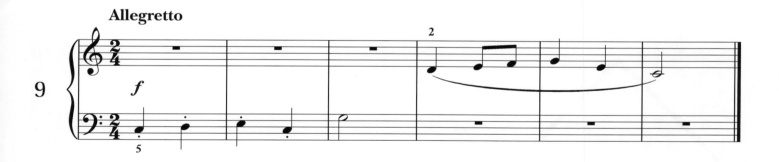

9 Allegretto

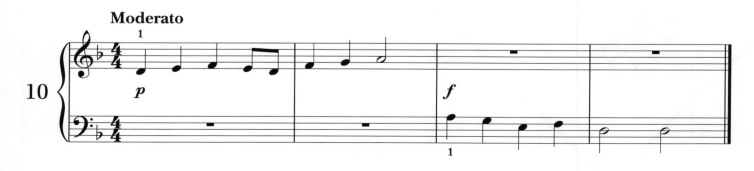

10 Moderato

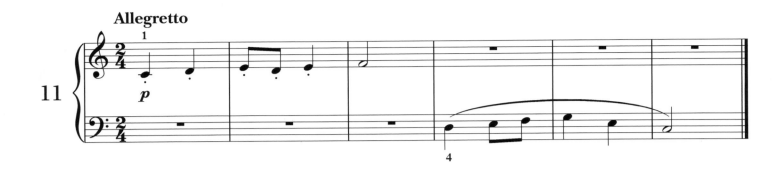

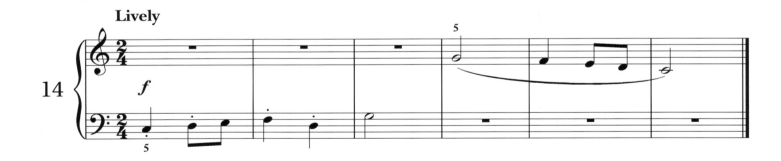

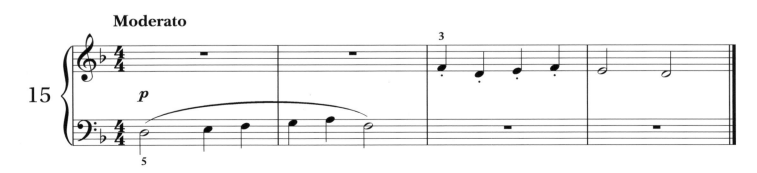

AB 4002

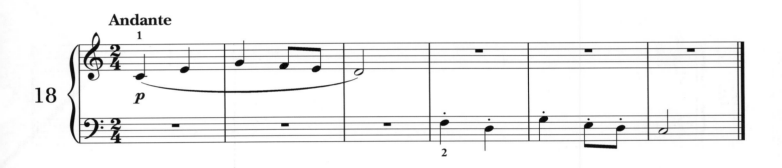

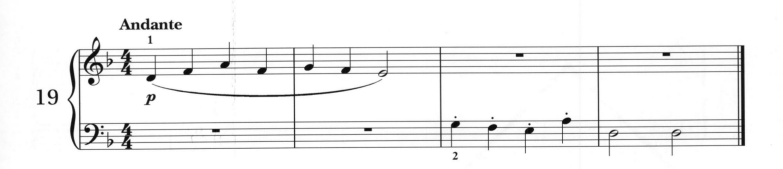

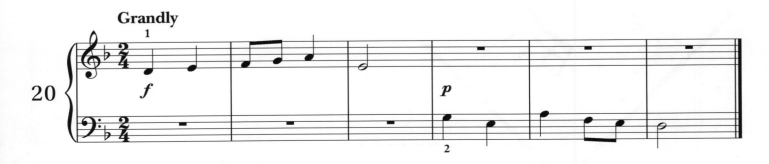

Andante

21

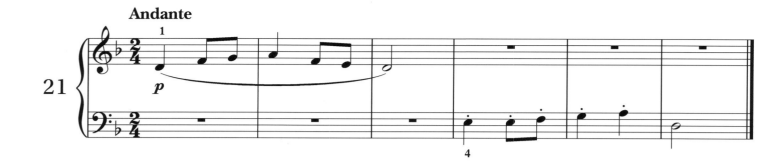

Grandly

22

Happily

23

Slowly

24

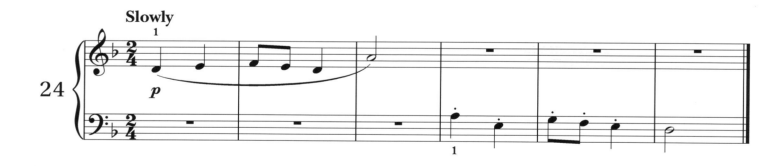

Allegretto

25

AB 4002

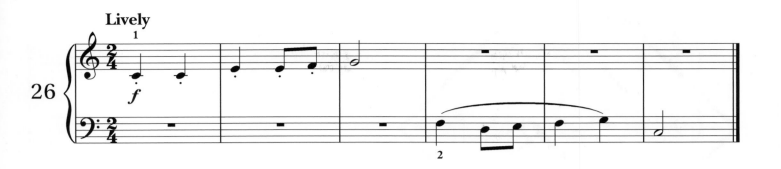

Lively

26

Lively

27

Allegretto

28

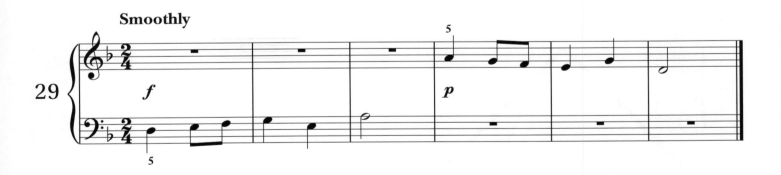

Smoothly

29

Moderato

30

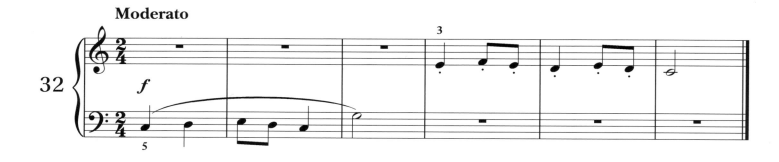

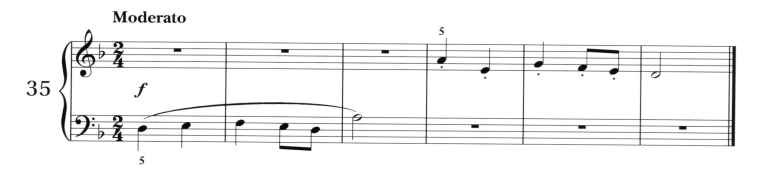